PAWS OFF...

...'COS

THIS BOOK BELONGS TO :-
NAME....James....Martin..............
ADDRESS....Old....Wick....farm.........
............No.11...............................

THE TOPPER BOOK

Printed and Published in
Great Britain by
D. C. Thomson & Co., Ltd.,
185 Fleet Street,
London, EC4A 2HS.

Tricky Dicky

DAD! YOUR TEA IS READY!

PAH! I CAN NEVER FIND HIM WHEN HIS TEA'S READY, AND IT GETS RUINED.

OHO! THINK I'LL GIVE MUM A "HELP"! HEH!

BURN! CINDER!

SO, TEATIME ON SUNDAY —

HAR! HERE WE GO, FOLKS.

PRESS!

I'M SINGING IN THE BATH... WARBLE! YORKS! WASSAT?

BLOOP! BLOOP!

LUNGE!

OI! TEA'S READY! HURRY UP!

YOU GUESSED! NOT REAL!

SPLICH!

EEK! I'M GOING!

SEND FOR **KELLY** AND HIS ASSISTANT, **CEDRIC**

IN THE STRANGE CASE OF

THE SUPER SHOPLIFTERS!

WHAT'S THIS? TALKING SHOP-DUMMIES? NO — IT'S NICK KELLY AND HIS ASSISTANT, CEDRIC, KEEPING A SECRET LOOK-OUT FOR SHOPLIFTERS!

LATEST STYLE

THIS STYLE £80

THIS STYLE £100

GENTS' OUTFITS

DON'T BAT AN EYE-LID, CEDRIC.

NO, MR KELLY! I'VE GOT MY PEEPERS ON THOSE TWO OVER THERE — LOOK!

SPLENDID, KELLY. THAT'S YOUR SIXTH ARREST THIS WEEK.

I DON'T THINK YOU'LL BE BOTHERED ANY MORE. WE'VE CRACKED THIS CASE.

THAT NIGHT —

IT'S FOR YOU.

AT THIS TIME OF NIGHT?

MEANWHILE.

SPARKLER'S JEWELLERS

HI LIFT LTD.

RIP!

ANOTHER JEWELLER'S NEATLY LIFTED! HO! HO!

RIGHT! LET'S GET IT TO OUR HIDE-OUT.

NEXT DAY —

I'M GOING TO USE THIS FAKE JEWELLERY AS SHOPLIFTERS' BAIT, INSPECTOR. WE'RE PUTTING IT ON SHOW AT JIFFANY'S THE JEWELLERS.

THAT NIGHT IN JIFFANY'S —

THE SHOPLIFTERS WILL SURELY BE TEMPTED BY ALL THOSE SPARKLERS.

YES! WE EVEN ADVERTISED THEM IN THE PAPERS.

SQUEEZE!

OOF!

GASP! WE'RE JAMMED AGAINST THE CEILING.

JIFFANY'S

RIP!

INSIDE —

GASP!

LOOK! KELLY'S COAT BUCKLE IS —

WHOO!

— ABOUT TO BURST THE BALLOON!

OO, 'ECK! THAT'S TORN IT!

BANG!

LET'S GO, BEFORE WE'RE RECOGNISED.

AFTER THEM, CEDRIC! THOSE COWS CAN GIVE US A LIFT.

THE ROAD GOES ROUND IN A BIG CURVE, SO WE CAN CUT STRAIGHT ACROSS AND GET AHEAD.

ON THE FAR SIDE OF THE FIELD —

BULLSEYE!

CRASH!

ONIONS

YOINK!

URCH!

HO! HO! I THINK THAT'S FIXED THE CROOKED PAIR, CEDRIC.

ONION NIFF

OOW!

OOW! MY EYES ARE STINGING! I CAN'T SEE.

DOWN AMONG THE DINOSAURS!

(SOME PREHISTORIC TALL TALES!)

FOXOSAURUS

The ancestor of the present-day fox, this pre-historic animal possessed a huge club-like tail, which it used with deadly effect on people-hunts. This gave rise to the well known expression "to give someone the brush-off"!

KANGOSAURUS

Early Australian settlers found this pre-historic kangaroo an ideal pitch-flattener for the local game of 'batty', the original form of cricket. However, attempts to teach it the game ended in failure, as the silly creature insisted on pocketing the ball — which just 'wasn't cricket'!

OSTRISAURUS

These ancient birds were trained by early African warriors to be wonderful war planes. However, after prolonged sky battles, with many feathers flying, they were grounded — just like their present day descendants, the ostrich.

ELEPHANTOSAURUS

When fully tamed and trained, these useful creatures were hot stuff as fire-engines. (Efforts to teach them TAP dancing ended in disaster, though).

TORTOSAURUS

This slow-moving creature wasn't SLOW to earn itself extra pocket-money! Stone Age shop-owners paid top prices for Tortosaurus shells, which converted nicely into a desirable 'shell-ter', or mini-supermarket!

NOW OPEN

WOAD ½ PRICE

BEARSKIN COATS REDUCED

DINOSAUR STEAKS

FLINTS FOR SALE

TROLLEYS

CHEESERY

MOUSOSAURUS

These most-timorous of all the dinosaurs were most unpopular because of their love of cheese. In their quest for a cheesy-bite they were liable to cause cave-ins in caves!

CAMELOSAURUS

Super-Hump, as it was named by man at the dawn of history, had five humps and, as a consequence, a terrific thirst. These giant guzzlers roamed the lush jungles of the Sahara, drinking the watering-holes dry. Soon the land became a parched waste of sand, sand and more sand.

SUDSY MALONE

THE SUPER-HERO WITH THE POWER-BATH!

AND FEATURING
PLUMB DUCK
HIS ASSISTANT.

SUDSY AND PLUMB ARE OUT ON PATROL IN THE BATHMOBILE AT CHRISTMAS, WHEN—

I'M DREAMING OF A WHITE CHRISTMAS . . . EH?

SHOOM!

LOOK! BLACK SNOW EVERYWHERE!

DOWN BELOW—

HAR! HAR! I HATE WHITE SNOW, SO I'M PAINTING IT BLACK!

REFILL PACK.

BLACK BOB.

SLOP!

HOI! STOP YOUR BLACK DEEDS, YOU VILLAIN! THAT'S NOT THE CHRISTMAS SPIRIT.

SHLUP!

YIPE! SUPER-HERO SUDSY MALONE! I'M OFF!

EEK! WE'VE GONE OUT OF CONTROL! . . . BLOOF!

UNK!

SKID!

SMASH!

'BYE-'BYE, MUGS! CACKLE!

LATER—

WHAT WOULD YOU LIKE FROM SANTA FOR CHRISTMAS, YOUNG SIR?

THAT'S EASY! MORE BLACK PAINT! HAW!

JINGLE-ME . . . JINGLE-ME . . .

TRICKY DICKY'S BIG GAG!

WILLIE FIXIT

HUNGRY

AT A FRIEND'S CHRISTMAS PARTY—

DOES ANYONE KNOW ANY GOOD PARTY GAMES?

I DO! MUSICAL CAKES!

EXPLAIN, HORACE!

IT'S EASY! JUST FORM A LINE AND PASS THESE CAKES ALONG — THEN, WHEN THE MUSIC STOPS, YOU EAT WHAT YOU HAVE.

THE GAME BEGINS—

HERE I COME.

SNIFF! SNIFF!

BLIND MAN'S DUFF? DON'T GET IT.

BUT HORACE DOES!

HEY! HE'S GRABBED THE CHRISTMAS PUD.

WELL, HE DID SAY IT WAS BLIND MAN'S DUFF.

PLUM DUFF! I LOVE IT.

LET'S PLAY A PROPER GAME.

HERE SHE IS!

ALL SQUEEZE IN LIKE SARDINES.

STILL ACTING SILLY.

ARE YOU THERE, CYNTHIA?

SOON—

EVERYONE'S HERE EXCEPT HORACE. WHY?

HE'LL BE AT THE GRUB!

JUST AS WE THOUGHT!

GRR!

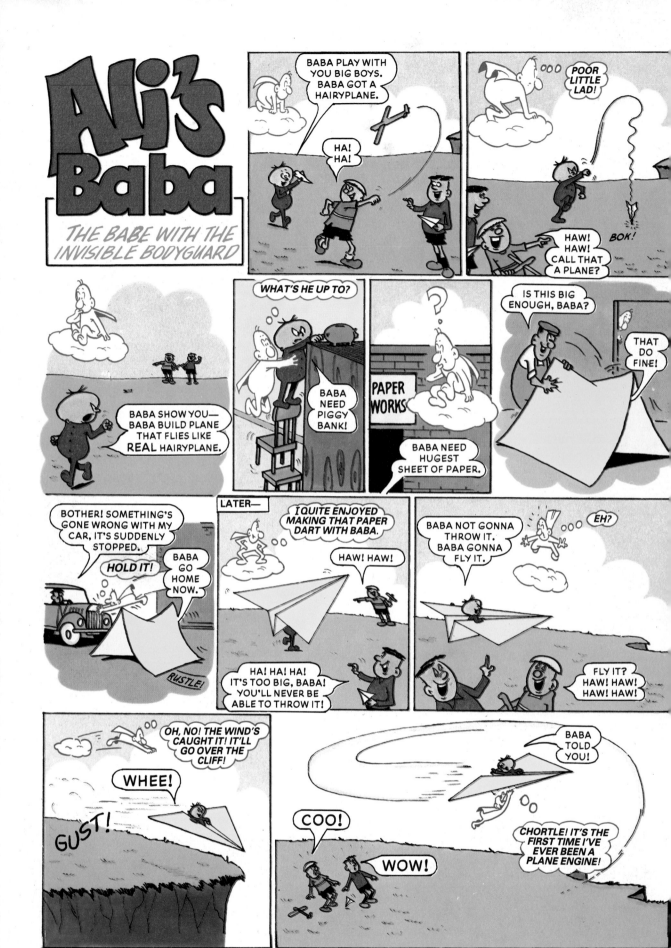

Brolly Good Fun
SOME NOT-YET-INVENTED UMBRELLAS!

Willie Walker and the Wonderful WHIZZERS from OZZ

In Workchester, England, young Willie Walker was busy putting the final touches to repairs on his bike.

THAT'S THAT! THE NEW TYRE MAKES MY BIKE SAFE TO USE AGAIN.

Then, suddenly, out of nowhere there appeared . . .

SHRIEK! A-A-A MONSTER!

But this monster could speak!

HO! HO! HO! DON'T WORRY, WILLIE! IT'S ONLY US!

Out of the "monster" stepped—

IT'S FADING! WHAT . . .? KRIK AND KRAK!

HELLO, WILLIE! IT'S GOOD TO BE BACK ON EARTH! DID OUR WHIZZ-PROJECTOR SCARE YOU? IT'S THE LATEST OZZ DEVICE. IT PROJECTS AN IMAGE OF WHATEVER THE WEARER IS THINKING ABOUT!

The Whizzer twins were friends of Willie's from the land of Whizz, on the far-off planet Ozz, which is a planet of high technology. Krik and Krak had just arrived in their amazing space car on a holiday visit to Earth. Later that day, Willie and his folks showed the visitors some family snaps . . .

THAT'S WILLIE'S UNCLE NICK IN HIS POLICE UNIFORM.

WHIZZO!

PHOTOGRAPHS ARE THE NEAREST IDEA WE HAVE TO YOUR WHIZZ-PROJECTOR!

Eventually—

YAWN! TIME FOR BED, I THINK. IT'S BEEN AN EXCITING DAY SINCE YOU TWO APPEARED.

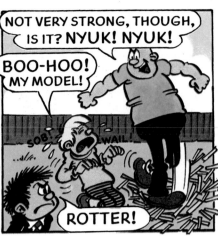

Jimmy Jinx
AND WHAT HE THINKS

JAMES! WAKEY-WAKEY! TIME TO GET UP!

YAWN! EH?

ERK! RIGHTO!

COME ALONG, JAMES! GET READY FOR SCHOOL!

NAW! TAKE A DAY OFF, JIM! BUT YOU'LL NEED TO BE READY TO ACT SICK WHEN MUM COMES IN.

YAWN! YEAH! IF I CAN STAY AWAKE LONG ENOUGH TO BE READY!

NEXT, PRACTISE YOUR "NOT VERY WELL" STAGGER FOR WHEN MUM COMES IN.

OOH! I'M EVER-SO-ILL!

BAH! WILL SOMEONE LISTEN TO ME?

STAGGER!

TSK! SILLY BOY! ANY MORE OF THIS AND YOU'LL END UP REALLY ILL!

TRIP!

BONK!

HERE SHE COMES! BE READY WITH YOUR "NOT WELL ACT", JIM!

KLOMP! KLOMP!

HMPH!

GREAT ACT, JIM!

OOH! OOH! I FEEL TERRIBLY UNWELL, I DO! OOH! OOH!

OH, DEAR!

Send for **KELLY** and his assistant **CEDRIC** IN THE CASE OF "BEAR-FACED ROBBERY"

BEARSDEN

TEDDY BEAR SALE

TWO DAYS BEFORE CHRISTMAS—

GO ON, ALGY — BUY ONE.

OH, DEAR, NO — I'D FEEL SILLY.

AT THE MINISTRY —

WHAT'S SO UNUSUAL ABOUT THE ROBBERIES, MINISTER?

THEY'RE UNUSUAL BECAUSE IT'S ALWAYS TEDDY-BEARS THAT ARE BEING STOLEN! I WANT IT STOPPED.

MEANWHILE, IN A NEARBY STORE —

STOP, THIEVES! DROP THOSE TEDDY-BEARS!

THEN —

LOOK — A TEDDY IN THAT WINDOW!

WE MUST HAVE IT. STAND BACK.

CRASH!

MEANWHILE —

MOST OF THE ROBBERIES HAVE HAPPENED IN DEPARTMENT STORES, CEDRIC. I'VE GOT A PLAN TO TRAP THE THIEVES.

DRESSED AS TEDDIES, MR MANAGER, WE'LL LIE IN WAIT — THEN POUNCE.

SUPA!

HERE, SARGE — TWO TEDDY-BEAR THIEVES. CASE CLOSED. 'BYE!

POLICE

BUT —

WHAT? ANOTHER TEDDY-BEAR ROBBERY? WE MUST HAVE GOT THE WRONG MEN.

SUPA TEDDY BEARS

I'M FIXING A HOMING DEVICE IN THIS VAN WE BORROWED.

BLEEP!

WE'RE HARD ON THEIR TRACK. TURN LEFT HERE, CEDRIC.

BLEEP!

STOP! THE VAN'S PARKED BEHIND THIS WALL.

IT SAYS "THE GAME'S UP. YOU'RE UNDER ARREST."

I DON'T GET IT.

YOU WILL IN A MINUTE, CHUM.

GOTCHA!

OW!

AND YOU!

SNAP.

CLICK!

— AND THE WORLD'S BIGGEST TEDDY-BEARS' PICNIC GETS UNDER WAY!

THANKS FOR LETTING US JOIN IN.

THIS IS THE NICEST CASE WE'VE EVER SOLVED, MR KELLY.

WE'LL TAKE ALL THE TEDDIES BACK AFTERWARDS.

HUNGRY HORACE

SLOBBER! GOBBLE! WHERE ARE YOU OFF TO, DAD?

I'M OFF TO A POSH DO — THAT'S WHY I'M WEARING MY DINNER JACKET.

A DINNER? LUCKY YOU!

LATER—

COME ON, HORACE— WE'RE GOING VISITING.

THAT'S MY BONE. GRR! IT'S A DOG'S LIFE WHEN HORACE IS HUNGRY.

SHOVE!

WHERE TO, MUM?

TO AUNTIE ELSIE'S.

AW, NO! NOT HER! YOU HARDLY GET ANYTHING TO EAT.

IT'S MY DINNER JACKET. IT'S BEST TO GO WELL SUPPLIED TO AUNTIE ELSIE'S!

CAKES.

CHEESE

BREADSTICKS!

DOUGHNUTS.

DRINKS.

BACK IN A JIFF.

WELL, HURRY!

ZIP!

HORACE! WHAT'S THAT?

YOWL! SCREECH!

THAT WOULDN'T HAPPEN WITH A FIDDLE, DADDY-BOOTS

NO!

HOW'S ABOUT A REAL FIDDLE, THEN, EH?

GROWL! NO!

LATER —

TIME FOR A CUPPA.

EH? WHASSAT

STUMBLE!

I'VE JUST REMEMBERED! WE'VE GOT UNCLE BERNARD'S BROKEN OLD VIOLIN — MAYBE THAT'LL SHUT YOU UP.

WOW! GREAT! TA, DAD!

NOW MAYBE I'LL GET SOME PEACE!

FAB! PERFECT!

When we say, "NEVER LOOK A GIFT HORSE IN THE MOUTH", we really mean, "Don't be critical of something you get for nothing." The saying comes from the practice of telling a horse's age by counting its teeth.

The saying "TO EAT HUMBLE PIE" began in the Middle Ages and is connected with venison. Only nobles and their guests ate the meat. The servants had a pie made from the offal or "umbles" of the deer. Therefore, someone who ate umble pie was a person of the lower classes. Nowadays, when someone admits that he is not as good as he claimed he was, he is said to "eat humble pie".

SO SAY

Long ago, it was believed that crocodiles wept and wailed as if in pain, so that when someone came to find out about the noise, the crafty crocodile could gobble them up. It was even believed that the crocodile shed tears over its victims, and from this came the saying, "CROCODILE TEARS", which means false or pretended tears.

Shepherds use their crooks or hooked sticks to rescue their sheep from all sorts of difficult situations. This has given rise to the saying "BY HOOK OR BY CROOK", which means to do something by any means at all.

When people are quarrelling, we often say that they are "AT LOGGERHEADS". The saying began in the days when loggerheads — metal balls on long handles — were used to melt tar. The tar-boys often used their loggerheads as weapons when they were fighting among themselves.

The saying "TO TOE THE LINE", means to obey orders. It came originally from the fact that runners at the start of a race had to obey the starter's order to "toe the line".

ALL OF US!

"TO BURY THE HATCHET" means to stop fighting or quarrelling. This saying comes from the old American Indian custom. When two tribes which had been at war with each other agreed to stop fighting, they used to bury all their war hatchets and other weapons to show that they were now at peace.

During the Battle of Copenhagen, in 1801, Horatio Nelson, whose squadron of twelve ships was being hard pressed, received the recall signal from his commander. Putting his telescope to his blind eye, Nelson declared that he could see no signal — and he continued the engagement, forcing the enemy to surrender. This action of Nelson's gave rise to the saying, "TO TURN A BLIND EYE", which means simply to ignore something because it does not suit us to notice it.

Willie Walker and the Wonderful WHIZZERS on Ozz

Willie Walker is on a return holiday visit to his space-pals' home in the land of Whizz, on the planet Ozz. Krik, Krak and Willie are about to compete in a Whizz version of a car treasure hunt. The Whizzer twins' teacher, Mr Nono, is in charge.

YOUR QUEST IS TO FIND THE 'UNSTOPPABLE RAINBOW'. HERE ARE YOUR CLUES, AND THE MAP FOR THE HUNT WILL APPEAR ON YOUR VISI-SCREENS AT REGULAR INTERVALS. GOOD LUCK, BOYS.

WHIZZO, MR NONO!

SOUNDS EXCITING!

The Whizzers' space-car zoomed through the city sky, making for a nearby jungle.

WHAT'S FIRST, TWINS? AND WHAT'S AN 'UNSTOPPABLE RAINBOW?'

HMM... 'FIND A PLACE WITH ONLY ONE! THERE TO CATCH AN EATABLE SUN!' GOT IT! GO NORTH-WEST, KRAK! TO THE WHIZZ-SUN TREE!

The chums sped towards a certain lone, jungle tree.

'AN EATABLE SUN' — THE ORANGE FRUIT OF THE TREE!

Next clue—

'SEARCH THE THREE-SIDED HILL, THEN TAKE WHATEVER YOU WILL.'

THIS PEBBLE WILL PROVE WE'VE BEEN HERE!

And the next—

GOT IT! THE STRIPED FEATHER OF THE WHIZZLY BIRD IS OUR NEXT PIECE OF EVIDENCE!

WELL CAUGHT, WILLIE!

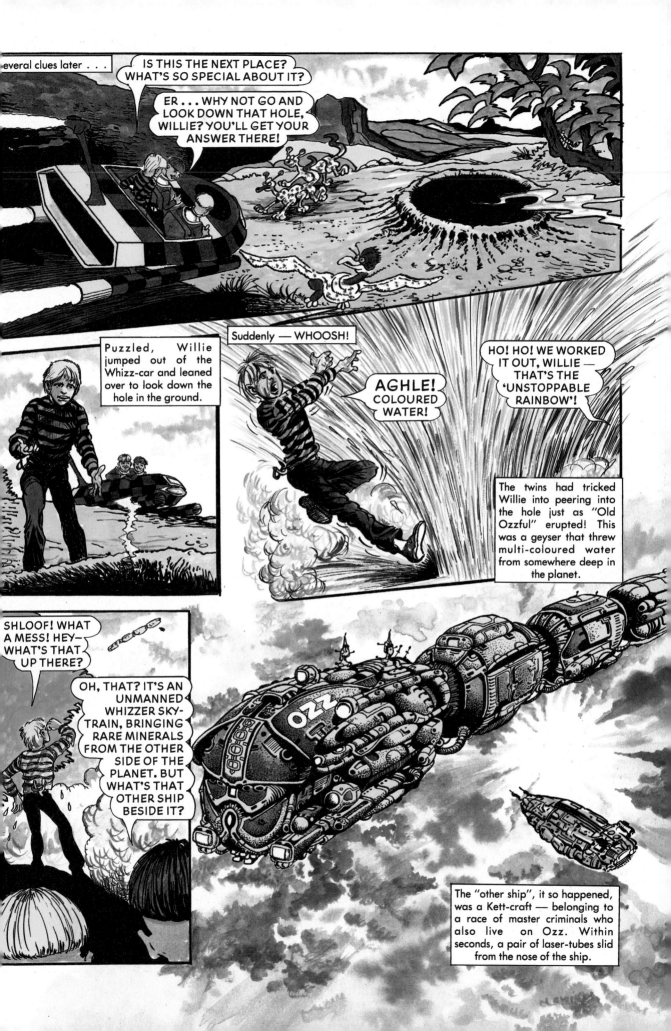

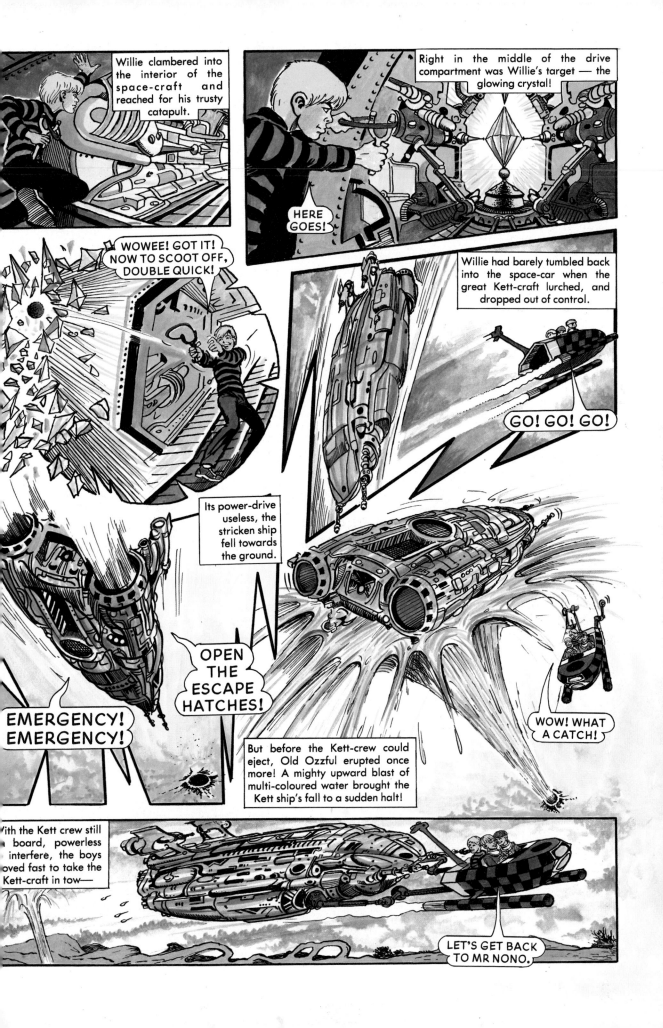

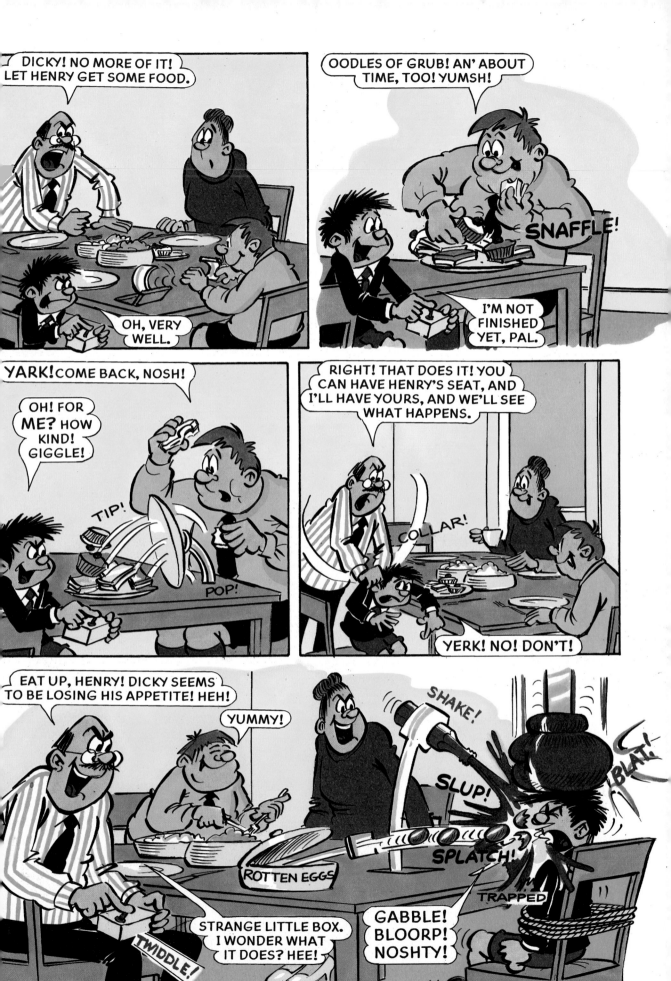

DESERT ISLAND DICK

— THE COMICAL CASTAWAY.

MORAL — PEOPLE WITH GLASS BOATS SHOULDN'T THROW COCONUTS!